Wise Publications
London/New York/Paris/Sydney/Copenhagen/Berlin/Madrid/Tokyo

Exclusive distributors:
Music Sales Limited
8/9 Frith Street, London W1D 3JB, England.
Music Sales Pty Limited
120 Rothschild Avenue, Rosebery, NSW 2018, Australia.

Order No. AM975711
ISBN 0-7119-9703-9
This book © Copyright 2002 by Wise Publications.

Music arrangements by Derek Jones.
Music processed by Paul Ewers Music Design.

Printed in the United Kingdom by
Caligraving Limited, Thetford, Norfolk.

www.musicsales.com

Your Guarantee of Quality:

As publishers, we strive to produce every book
to the highest commercial standards.

While endeavouring to retain the original running
order of the recorded album, the book has been
carefully designed to minimise awkward page turns
and to make playing from it a real pleasure.

Particular care has been given to specifying
acid-free, neutral-sized paper made from pulps which
have not been elemental chlorine bleached.

This pulp is from farmed sustainable forests and
was produced with special regard for the environment.

Throughout, the printing and binding have been
planned to ensure a sturdy, attractive publication
which should give years of enjoyment.

If your copy fails to meet our high standards,
please inform us and we will gladly replace it.

time of my life 4
cloud 9 10
never forgotten 19
leave me be 24
lady let me shine 30
stupid games 48
following the sun 36
only desire 42
promised tide 53
the midas touch 60
some kind of wonderful 68

time of my life

Words & Music by Joseph Washbourne

1. Sit-ting in the sum-mer sun,___ bid-ing my time,___ wait-ing for the de-mons to go a-way.___
(Verse 2 see block lyric)

8

Verse 2:
Woke up in the morning rain
God knows where I slept again
No recollection of the night
Oh God, what's this I see
You lying next to me
With a smile on your face
So we're alright
Yes we're alright.

'Cause I had the time of my life *etc.*

9

cloud 9

Words & Music by Joseph Washbourne

Don't try to com - fort me____ 'cause I'm___ not home___

right now.___

Oh._____

2. I can feel___ the heat with - in___ your fire____ breath, so

(Verse 3 see block lyric)

Verse 3:
I can hear you listening at my door
But I won't let you in
You can huff and puff
And blow my door down, right now.

Cloud nine is a place *etc.*

never forgotten

Words & Music by Joseph Washbourne

1. I reached you oh,__ so ve - ry late,_____ yeah._____
(Verse 2 see block lyric)

Al - rea - dy wait - ing at the gate, yeah.

The pic - tures on the wall, they re - mind us all things have got to change or else they still re - main.

It's got to change.

You had it all but it broke your heart. You want it all

Verse 2:
I could not have done any more, yeah
Already walking through the door, yeah
But the pictures on the wall
They remind us all
That things have got to change
Or else they still remain
It's got to change.

You had it all *etc.*

leave me be

Words & Music by Joseph Washbourne

1. Dif - f'rent col - ours and dif - fer - ent at - mos - pheres.

Verse 2:
I wander up, I wander down
I find it hard, you being around.

If you think I don't mean it *etc.*

lady let me shine

Words & Music by Joseph Washbourne

We're just

And oh,___ who knows_ where the wind_ may take_ us,

just as long as love_ don't break_ us, la-dy let me shine_____ for you._

Oh,___ walked a thou-sand miles_ to drink_ your wa-ter

Verse 2:
Lady, I don't know where you've been
Lord only knows just what you've seen
Lady, I still don't know where you are
So very near, so very far.

Oh we're just drifting away
On the dawn of a new day.

Who knows where the wind may take us *etc.*

following the sun

Words & Music by Julian Deane & Timothy Woodcock

1. Sun - day morn - ing, day - light break - ing, no - thing's stop - ping me__ from smil-
(Verse 2 see block lyric)

Verse 2:
Heading east, I'm looking skyward
Start to think that maybe I could
Reach the rising sun
And catch her when she falls
Sunday evening, daylight broken
Nothing stopping me from smiling
Just a fleeting glimpse
And everything is fine.

But this ain't what I planned *etc.*

only desire

Words & Music by Joseph Washbourne & Julian Deane

yes - ter - day's fire, words that were writ - ten, but words they were on - ly de-

- sire.

Cadd9

Gadd9

On - ly_____ de - sire._____

Gadd9

Pic - tures you've paint - ed of yes - ter - day's dreams.__ E-

(Verse 2 see block lyric)

Cadd9

-mo - tions a - live, but no - one will see their de - sire._____

come now and sit by the fire._____ May - be it's on - ly de-

- sire._____ May - be it's on - ly de - sire.

Verse 2:
Picking up pieces I threw on the fire
Words became letters
But letters were only desire
Only desire.

Lady, I don't want to fight *etc.*

47

stupid games

Words & Music by Joseph Washbourne

1. When all the boats had left the shore_
(Verse 2 see block lyric)
___ a thou - sand peo - ple may - be more,___ as the sun___ burnt through their eyes___

Verse 2:
History passed me by at school
But I, by no means play the fool
The past and present melt to one
But the future now has gone
And I guess one would assume
That there's nothing else to lose.

No more science left to bend
The world was flat, we reached the end
The other side now maybe nice
Now's your turn to roll the dice
And then everybody's still
But I can't help but feel

It's such a shame, we all feel the pain *etc*

promised tide

Words & Music by Joseph Washbourne

1. Yeah.

I can't be - lieve_____ what I have seen,_____ a girl that I know_____ from_____

_____ a dream. She is the one,_____ though she don't__ know, and

I must find out__ where she's__ to go.

Glock 8va

54

Verse 3:
When I find that which is naturally mine
I sail from the harbour out to sea
I follow the map that I drew in a dream
To the land where you fell in love with me
To a place where you chose to be with me.

I will sail *etc.*

the midas touch

Words & Music by Joseph Washbourne

some kind of wonderful

Words & Music by John Ellison

Verse 2:
When I hold her in my arms
She sets my soul on fire
Ooo, when my baby kisses me
My heart becomes filled with desire
When she wraps her lovin' arms around me
It drives me out of my mind
Oh, when my baby touched me
Chills run up and down my spine
Well, my baby, she's alright
Well, my baby, she's clean outta sight
Let me tell you 'bout her.

She's some kind of wonderful *etc.*